First published in Great Britain 2000
This edition published 2003
by Egmont Books Limited
239 Kensington High Street, London W8 6SA

ISBN 1 4052 0468 0

1 3 5 7 9 10 8 6 4 2

Printed in Italy

Pooh clutches his Special Pencil
Case and walks home with Piglet.
What a lucky bear!

There is even a rubber and a
ruler. And the Special Case
shuts with a click when
you close it.
"Thank you!"
growls Pooh
happily.

Pooh holds up the present.
It is a Very Special Pencil Case,
with pencils in it marked 'B' for
Bear, 'HB' for Helping Bear and
'BB' for Brave Bear.

At last the parcel is undone.
Pooh nearly falls over, he is
so pleased.
"Let me see! Let me see!"
says Roo, jumping up and down.

Everybody is very
excited. They want
to know what is
inside the parcel.
"Open it, Pooh!
What is it?" they say.
Pooh tries to open it
as quickly as he can,
but without cutting
the string. After all,
you never know
when a bit of string
might be Useful.

When all the food has
been eaten, Christopher
Robin bangs on the table
with his spoon.
"Listen, everybody!" he
says. "This is a party for
Pooh, the best bear in all
the world. I've got a
present for him. Pass it
down to silly old Pooh!"

Eeyore thinks it will rain.
Roo is very excited. He has
never been to a party before.
"Hello, Pooh!" he squeaks.
"Hello, Piglet!"
"Now, now, dear," says Kanga.
"Drink up your milk first, and
talk afterwards."

Christopher Robin, Pooh,
Eeyore, Piglet, Owl, Kanga
and Roo, Rabbit and all his
friends and relations arrive
at the party.

"Eeyore," says Owl. "Christopher Robin is giving a party. He would like you to come."
"Are you sure?" says Eeyore.
"Of course," says Owl. "He wants everybody to be there."

Owl isn't sure
about that and
flies off to find
the others.

Owl flies off into the Hundred
Acre Wood. First of all he
meets Pooh.
"Pooh," he says. "Christopher
Robin is giving a party especially
for you!"
"A party for me?" says Pooh.
"Will there be those little cake
things with pink sugar icing?"

Christopher Robin is going to give a party. He tells Owl that it is going to be a special party for Pooh.
"When will it be?" asks Owl.
"Tomorrow," says Christopher Robin. "Will you tell Pooh and all the others as quickly as you can?"

A Party for Pooh

From the stories by A. A. Milne

A Party for Pooh

This book
belongs to:

....